SOMETHING YOU SHOULD KNOW

The Fulfillment of Your Heart's True Desire

by

Clement Watt

FOUR STAR BOOKS, Incorporated
Publishers

128 SW "I" Street
Grants Pass, Oregon 97526
Office 541-955-2742
Fax 541-955-2745

Privately published and distributed by
Clement Watt, circa 1919

In 1919, the United States was celebrating the end of a World War. Soldiers returned home with dreams of prosperity, wives and mothers looked ahead to new security and comforts, schoolchildren dreamed of a bright future. But — unbeknownst to most — the country was already on the path to the Great Depression. The era that greeted them, the Roaring Twenties, was a decade of moral and financial collapse, and those caught in this time became known as the Lost Generation.

Many of us are still lost. We seek the fulfillment of many of the dreams that were born with our ancestors. For all such seekers, this manuscript holds the key. Picture if you will a great American industrialist and philanthropist, wealthier than Andrew Carnegie and wiser than Solomon, addressing his workers and their families in 1919. Let us call him "Clement Watt". He knows what they yearn for. He knows that they — like many of us — have sought answers in all the highly publicized motivational literature of the time, and remain deeply discouraged. He knows what they must do.

Here is his message:

❧

"I am large, I contain multitudes."

— Walt Whitman, *Song of Myself*

ONE WAR IS OVER, and another begins. "What?" you are saying to yourself, "Is this fellow mad? We are at peace!" True, our young men are no longer spilling blood in distant lands, but are we — are you — at peace? Or are you merely fighting another, less visible enemy? You awake each morning, do you not, in a profound state of distress. If you are a soldier just returned, you look about at the four walls and plead aloud, "Let this be my lucky day." Then you drag yourself about, preparing for the drudgery of another workday at the factory, or the office, or some other enclosure where you expect to pound away at the same dull task minute after slow minute, dreaming all the while of a better life. If you are a young lady, perhaps the wife of this self same cheerless worker, you awake with empty prospects, to the routine that repeats itself endlessly: a succession of domestic tasks which are invaluable for maintaining the simple comforts of common life, but nonetheless void of all vitality.

Like your mate, you are wishing, "Let this be my lucky day." If you are a youth, whose eyes open to schoolbooks lying forsaken on the bedside table, you too see hours of monotonous academic toil ahead, and wonder at the worth of parsing sentences and adding great columns of numbers. You look at your father and mother, and sigh for your fate. "Let this be my lucky day," you whisper.

While you wish for a measure of luck to offset your travail, you know that there is little enough of good fortune to go around. You wonder what to think. You wonder how to better your lot. As if to feast on your distress, a multitude of self-appointed experts and authorities rushes in with answers. They issue you instructions. They promise solutions to life's problems.

Open a newspaper on any morning, and there are headlines and advertisements insisting upon what you should decide and how you must behave. The editor has his say, telling you to vote for the Income Tax, or reject the Treaty of Versailles, or fight Prohibition. If you will only do what I am telling you, he declares, the world will be a better place. Don't think for yourself, he warns, let me do it for you. The advertisers have their say, hawking potions that cure all aches and pains, and all manner of products that "no one can live without."

We seem scarcely able to keep from mimicking this pomposity that greets us day after day. On streets all through the city, as the men trudge off to the factory or tramp home; as the women congregate at their kitchen windows, stringing the family's laundry into the stale city air; as youth on the verge of adulthood make their way out of the schoolyard, all are full of great pretenses. Everywhere, they are discussing with great animation, but little originality or understanding, the featured issues of the day, or bragging about the latest gadget they have gotten, or gloating over some slight appreciation from a boss or a teacher. All — nearly without exception — are judging as they have been told to judge, desiring what they have been told to desire, revering who and what they have been told to revere, all in the service of pretending to know what life is all about.

There is no fulfillment in any of this. It amounts to a great noise. Rather than celebrating their vitality and human potential, all of these people are — as Henry David Thoreau so wisely pronounced — leading lives of quiet desperation. They are simply following instructions that say, "Remain unhappy, ignorant, and anxious, but pretend that you are not."

These observations lead me to conclude that, while such citizens are no longer at war with the armies of other nations, they remain in an empty, futile struggle with a far more formidable enemy: They are at war with themselves. Each, seeking words to live by, finds none but empty commonplaces that can bring no lasting comfort. All continue to end each day cursing themselves for not "measuring up", and see life stretch before them as a barren calendar of empty toil. They perceive that, all around, others rise in the world toward greater wealth and ease — or so it seems.

To conceive a strategy for winning this great internal war between who you are and who you would be, let us take a lesson from a hero of the war with Spain that closed the last century. I am referring to one Lieutenant Rowan of the U.S. Army, who has been celebrated in Mr Elbert Hubbard's *A Message to Garcia*.[†]

Rowan had developed a reputation for following orders, no questions asked. The Bureau of Military Intelligence conceived a mission which only a fellow the likes of Rowan might accept. He was asked by President McKinley to march through the treacherous Cuban jungle and deliver a sealed envelope to the leader of the patriot forces, General Garcia. Rowan accepted and com-

[†] EDITOR'S NOTE: *Clement Watt is referring here to a brief essay published originally in 1899, and perhaps familiar to the 1919 audience he addresses.*

pleted the mission. Mr Hubbard glorifies Rowan's willingness to *march straight into the unknown*. All of us must agree with him on this score, certainly. I would hope that Mr Hubbard, himself the unfortunate victim of the sinking of the *Lusitania*[†], would welcome my effort here to take his lesson even further, to develop a moral for our time.

The world is much too full of men who spend their lives without taking a step in any direction, afraid even to have a thought that is not already branded on the common mind of ordinary humanity. Whatever popular idea is in the air, that he will suck up, and the stale atmosphere with which he fills himself maintains the hollowness of his being. Take as an example an adage that you have no doubt heard, originally penned by the famous American biographer of Horace Greeley, James Parton. Mr Parton has written "fidelity is seven-tenths of business success." An utterly paralyzing

[†] EDITOR'S NOTE: *The* Lusitania *was a British ocean liner sunk by a German submarine on May 7, 1915. This event influenced the eventual American entry into World War I.*

statement, to be sure. Think of the figure it portends, a businessman who is so set in his ways, so caught up in living each day as an act of fidelity to the same principles, methods, and products that he worshipped the day before, that in practice he will not ever have a new thought. He lives in a rut. And think of this captain of industry's clerk, who spends each day as a doltish yes-man, fearful that any breech of fidelity to the stale enterprise he supports will cost him a livelihood, and prohibit all chance of his rising to the same heights of inaction, that great Mount Olympus of stubborn turpitude, that his superior occupies. Ask either of them, the employee or the employer, what accounts for their unswerving devotion to mental immobility, and they will surely reply with a symptom of that disease, the cliché that has become a motto for the masses who must justify their fear of the unknown. In one way or another, both of them will echo Mr Parton's sentiments, and then settle back into the safe confines of their "fidelity".

I hope that you are now saying to yourself, "Wait one moment, Mr Watt. You say that Lieutenant Rowan deserves Hubbard's praise for marching into the unknown, yet you castigate those who avoid the new and unknown out of misplaced adherence to the popular principle of fidelity. Was not Lieutenant Rowan's act one of pure fidelity?"

I reply to your questioning thoughts, "If Lieutenant Rowan can be called a hero, it is not because of his blind fidelity to his country, or to his superior officers, or to military tradition. To march into a dangerous jungle because one has been taught to follow orders is merely an act of obedience, and when we merely obey, we are no better than dumb animals who run and fetch out of fear, or habit, or sheer stupidity. If Lieutenant Rowan can be called a hero, it is because of his fidelity to *the unknown*, the courage to follow his instincts into action *with no guarantee of the consequences*. If Lieutenant Rowan can be called a hero, it is because he welcomed what all others called impossible."

Sad to say, the lesson of fidelity to the unknown is too often misapplied. In that misapplication lie most of the world's ills. In its correction lies their remedy.

Permit me to illustrate. Picture if you will the head of a large business enterprise, whose daily obsession is keeping his employees industrious and obedient. He reads of Lieutenant Rowan, and his reasoning goes thus: Just as Lieutenant Rowan marched obediently into the Cuban jungle, an office clerk should do what he is told. But if you are the poor clerk who works under such an employer, you will find that you are being faithful not to the great unknown, but to your role as a servile functionary. You see, Rowan's task was a clearly significant matter of life and death; the clerk's task seems a purposeless bit of scribbling. Rowan is asked to set off for parts unknown; the clerk is asked to repeat the familiar, day after day.

Rowan is asked to lead an expedition; the clerk is asked to remain a mere assistant on call. Rowan's reward is honor and glory; the clerk's reward — should he prove his mettle in his drudgery — is an even greater future share of dull, pointless tasks.

The danger for the poor clerk is that he will eventually become convinced — mainly because he is dependent upon his paycheck — that there is something heroic about gritting one's teeth, sitting at one's work station, and becoming a stoic expert at redundancy.

The clerk and his wife will one day raise a son, who will stand at the age of fourteen before a stern but quite ordinary schoolteacher. The boy has, apparently, failed to follow this academician's directions precisely, and the teacher is dismayed. "Remember my boy," says the teacher, "that the ability to follow the instructions of a superior, without veering from them, elaborating them, or extending them in any way, is requisite to secure employment. Imagination will get you no bread." This boy is being taught, as should be evident, how to be a common clerk, just like his father.

Picture now a mother giving her daughter advice on the eve of the young lady's marriage to the aforementioned clerk: "Your domestic responsibilities are few and well-defined," she says earnestly. "They will, after a time, prove less than interesting. It is then that you must devote yourself even more assiduously to the requirements of your station. Dream if you must of greater wealth and richer society. But keep to your place and duties, taking comfort in the fact that a household, well-maintained, is your contribution to the welfare of your husband and the greatness of our nation." The daughter murmurs these words to herself daily, but they offer her no felt reward.

Perhaps at this moment you are seeing something of yourself in this clerk, or his wife, or his son. Then, my dear friend, it is absolutely crucial that you attend to the advice I am about to give. Instead of habituating yourself to empty obedience, I want you to learn to listen, to question, and to dream. Unlike the many who stumble blindly from disappointment to disappointment, you must learn to listen to the inner voice that knows right action. Unlike those herded through the years of their existence like dumb, driven cattle, you must learn to question mediocrity, and give no quarter to dullness. Unlike those who merely sleep through every hour, even with their eyes open, you must learn to bring the vivid promise of your potential into actuality.

How do I achieve this, you ask? This is, I am afraid, the wrong question, if with it you are expecting some set of instructions guaranteed to improve your lot. As the illustrations which I have presented attest, the whole world of ordinary thinkers cries out instructions to you day after day, and their words come to nought but more human desperation. This is because so few understand that there is but *one way* to take control of your occupation and life. I will illustrate that way for you, with the hope that you will immediately begin travelling its path. Be advised, however, that what I have to tell you runs counter to common business, domestic, and academic practices. Indeed, what I have to tell you runs counter to common thought itself!

I shall begin these next remarks with primary attention to the worker who earns the daily bread, and shall proffer to him some perceptions about the common run of business behavior, with a view to transforming him into a most uncommon worker. The principles that apply to this worker will also benefit the young woman fretting over domestic toil and the student beleaguered by dull ciphers. Their plights will enter our discussion as we proceed.

Look around you in any place of business, and what is everyone doing, from the chief executive down to the mail clerk? Each of them stops a dozen times or more each hour: the boss pulls a gold timepiece from his pocket; the clerk stares up at the clock on the wall; the line worker asks the time of his fellow. All have one goal in view, the end of the day. All come into the office each morning with a single purpose, *to leave it*. All — even the most senior and well-paid — find their place of employment detestable, and though they would not admit this, their ridiculous obsession with time tells the tale.

The desire to leave off work is not usually the result of bad conditions, although it is true that few employers care whether their offices or factories are conducive to good service. As I have attested, quite truthfully, even the great man ensconced in the executive suite checks his watch regularly. He is obeying common sense, which has told him, first of all, that business must be drudgery; secondly, that wherever he is not must be better than where he is; and thirdly, that time is a commodity which must be consumed as quickly as possible. And so, the object of everyday life becomes to *kill time*. This is certainly madness, for as we all know, at the end of our time in this world lies death; those constantly checking their watches are mentally accelerating toward the grave.

Now imagine if you will a small apartment, nicely furnished and impeccably kept. The lady of the house leaves her appointed tasks at frequent intervals, and darts into the sitting room to look at the small clock sitting on the mantel. At least twice each day, she assures herself that it is well-wound. In the occasional conversation with a neighbor, this lady will make sure to ask the time, without making her obsession too obvious. "My, it must be getting late," she will say, and then wait for the other to consult her own timepiece and answer, "Dear, dear, it is only ____ o'clock." Whereupon our lady will invent some pretense to hurry home and check the accuracy of the display of time in her own quarters.

Now turn your attention to the local secondary school. Here the tyranny of the clock is especially absurd, for here the whole of human knowledge is divided into segments. During segment one, the students must focus on mathematics, cleansing their minds of all thoughts not pertaining to numbers. Segment two is devoted to history, and the rehearsal of names and dates is the exclusive task. Segment three is devoted to literature, with the instructor droning about the glories of Homer's poetry, and giving regular reprimands to those whose attention seems to be wandering. And so the day proceeds, segment giving way to segment, in strict adherence to the schedule mandated by the local board of education. What is foremost in the mind of the young student trapped in these confines? The clock. He watches the passage of minute after painful minute, too often oblivious to the instructor's voice.

With these scenes in mind, let us consider the sentiments of the great writer John Ruskin, who has said that "A fool wants to kill space and time; a wise man, first to gain them, then to animate them." Toward gaining and animating the time of our lives, no one at Watt Industries carries a time-piece, and there are no clocks on the desks or walls. I ask only that my associates begin work when the sun has risen to the treetops in the east, and leave work at some point during the sun's descent whenever each feels as if his accomplishments for the day have been substantial, and sees that the day's enterprise will be no poorer for his departure. Reader, you say to yourself now, "But these requirements are not clear. How is one to assess his accomplishments?" And I answer that any individual will acquire this ability once given the chance. For the moment, understand that the primary goal is not to *finish* the workday, or even to *finish* a particular task, although these phenomena will occur naturally enough. Those intent upon *finishing* forget where they are, who they are, and what they are doing. I say pointedly to each of my associates, and to each of you: Your primary responsibility is to do the task with full awareness of what you are doing, engaged in the present moment of your experience. When you hammer a nail, feel each strike; when you turn the page of a ledger or a book, feel the fiber of the paper between your fingers; when you speak, listen to the music of your utterance; when another speaks to you, listen with your whole being; when you take a step, feel the weight of your body press against the sole of your foot; when you think, watch your thoughts.

When you can do these things with regularity, you will have achieved the great power that all ordinary people fear: *Autonomy*. It is Autonomy that will assure not only excellence at work, at school, and in your home, but also a life that is truly free. Let us consider the origins of this important word, Autonomy. It comes to us from the classical Greek roots *auto*, or "self" and *nomos*, or "law". Autonomy, then, is self-government. The autonomous individual is the maker of his own laws.

However, your life to this point has been full of others making the laws of your behavior and attitudes. Your mind is full of these "laws", which appear to you as common thoughts, but which are really powerful and often destructive commands. Consider just one of these, which has no doubt been repeated to you since childhood, by parents and bosses and relatives and friends, the very "law" that makes the absence of clocks at Watt Industries seem so curious. I am referring to the well-known saying, "Time is the stuff between pay days", a thought that renders each day spent at work into an empty stretch of mere waiting, rather than an episode of vitality. Realize that this law has taken residence in your mind as an incontestable thought, and that it has determined much of your anxiety and unhappiness. Every worker who believes this begins each work day equating time spent on the job only with the sum of money he will receive at week's end. Thus his attention is diverted from the substance of his activity to its by-product, and he works in a state of distraction, counting the minutes to day's end, tracking the hours to week's end. What is the quality of his accomplishment while this thought rules his behavior? Poor. What is the condition of his spirit while this thought rules his attitude? Poor.

Let us consider the plight of those who spend each day working not for money, but in the case of our poor clerk's wife, for the maintenance of essential human comforts; and in the case of our schoolboy, for the acquisition of knowledge. What are the common thoughts that rule the day of each? They are many, to be sure. Each day is flooded with a torrent of common thoughts, tugging us this way and that; scarcely a moment passes without our being in the grip of one of them. However, it will do me no good here to overwhelm you with examples. Such a strategy would only frighten you, and rightly so. For if we looked truly at the quality of our thoughts and the life they are prescribing, we would be altogether horrified.

Foregoing horror for illumination, let us remain with the theme we have established, that is, the to lengthen the school day). Beleaguered by this thought, our young scholar finishes an hour of mathematics instruction presuming that he must be, or should be, one hour wiser. But indeed, quite the opposite is true. The time spent drilling on this academic segment has him feeling one hour more ignorant, believing as he does that a young man who cannot recite formulas with facility is a young man who has not learned and cannot think. Thus, he thinks of time as a wholesale enemy: it passes so slowly as to make academic toil seem an endless thing, and the intellectual profit that time is said to promise manifests itself as a deficit instead. Sadly, many of our modern schoolrooms are well-equipped with clocks, each one looming above the door frame as if to emphasize that it governs the entrances and exits of all occupants. I have been told by a gloating Superintendent of Public Instruction that before too long, there will be no schoolroom without a clock. Perhaps if we put a stop to such "progress", and freed our students from their chronometric overseers, our young people might make a beginning at Autonomy.

Indeed, Autonomy is the relief for this poverty of body, mind, and soul that we continue to observe in all these scenes. You must discharge the "lawful" thoughts that brutalize you, and learn to define the virtue of what you do in your own way. The achievement of Autonomy derives from an allied principle, one no less strange to the populace at large. This is *Anomaly*. From the Greek again, we learn that Anomaly means "without *nomos*" [without law]. An anomalous individual is one who deviates from the common *nomos*, that is, those paralyzing rules and laws that fill our thoughts and govern our every moment. The worker or wife or student who completes even one hour without checking the clock is enacting Anomaly, and anyone who leads a life of anomalies has achieved Autonomy.

※

THERE IS PERHAPS no circumstance more Anomalous in a place of business, or a home, or a schoolroom, than the absence of clocks and the evasion of the tyranny of time. Yet let me venture another affront to "common sense" which is perhaps more striking. I am now speaking directly to those of you who are new to my workforce, and I am making what you will regard as a strange promise, to wit: *When you join Watt Industries, you will have no job.* You wonder, "Is this statement not a patent contradiction? I am being given employment, but no job?" Yes, this is precisely the case, and once you get beyond your common sense of "job", you will see that such a situation is a tremendous benefit. A "job", after all, is something like a prison sentence.

Let us say that I hire you as a scrivener, and indicate the scope of your responsibility precisely, as the copying of official documents at the behest of your executive officers, neatly and without error, day after day, without comment or suggestion, meeting all assigned deadlines, until such time as you develop scrivener's palsy, whereupon you will be retired with a pension sufficient for a meager existence as you draw toward your last breath. Many would respond with gratitude to such an assignment. It provides a steady income, they reason, offers clear parameters of satisfactory achievement, and does not require undue exertion. Most importantly, it furnishes a title: "Scrivener". "I am a scrivener," such a fellow tells his friends decisively. "My husband is a scrivener," says his wife to her neighbor, with a solid and appreciative sense of their station in life. Asked about the general goings-on at his place of employment, such a fellow pleads ignorance: "I know not what the others are up to, nor do I care. I am a scrivener." Questioned about the kinds of documents with which he deals, he protests, "Their meaning is none of my concern, so long as the copy is clean. I am a scrivener." The mind of this fellow is like a small room with no windows, as is his spirit. Mind and spirit are confined with his body inside of his job and its official, invariable title: Scrivener. Promotion to a position of greater responsibility and greater rewards is impossible, for his job has barred him from knowing any other world.

All of you who are reading this will, I trust, realize the great wrong of defining yourself and your worth with a single, small label. The trouble with this is patently illustrated with our scrivener, but it is equally present for the young lady and the schoolboy whose regression into gloom and despair we have been tracking. How does the young lady identify herself? Surely, she calls herself a "housewife", and it is probably true that early in her career as such, she couched her identity in glowing terms, seeing herself as Mr Ruskin described her in his *Political Economy*: "the good housewife taking pride in her pretty table-cloth, and her glittering shelves." Sadly but truly, however, the condition of one's table-cloth and shelves does not remain a rich reward for very long. With her world confined to matters of domestic hygiene, her mind tells our young lady that she must be proud of her title, "housewife", that she must not aspire to other worldly or intellectual ambitions. She reads a little, but not so much as to seem above her station. She expresses interest in her husband's occupation, but not such curiosity that distracts her from the daily routine. She avoids altogether matters of finance and politics, and speaks for the most part with other housewives about their common duties and interests. She thinks that doing anything more would be, to cite the tyranny of the clock once again, a waste of time. Thus, she will never be other than the label that holds her fast, "housewife".

What of our young student? He too carries a label that defines his self-worth. He is, quite plainly, a "student". Now this would be a fine label if it entailed the true richness and excitement of learning. However, in the mind of our young man rests a quite common and dull definition of "student". A student, he has been told by his teachers and parents and clergyman, obeys without questioning, follows the well-worn path of convention and tradition, and only traffics in well-established and well-known facts. With this sense of himself in mind, our student resists anything genuinely *interesting* that crosses his mind. As he watches a history teacher point out the territory of the Louisiana Purchase on a map of these United States, our young man, fresh from a mathematics class in which he had been tracing geometric figures which illustrate the Pythagorean theorem, begins to imagine a giant triangle: one leg is the Mississippi River itself, the base is our southern border extending from New Orleans westward, and the great hypotenuse extends from the Western tip of Lake Superior to the southern coast of California. He begins to envision a trade route along this hypotenuse, a road that would cut across both the great high plains and the vistas of the southwest. His vision is interrupted by a rap on the knuckles, and his punishment for imagining the unknown is to write five hundred times in his tablet, "The Louisiana Purchase was completed in 1803." As he serves his sentence, our prisoner tells himself, "I am a student, and this I must do," and proceeds. The young man had dared to enact an Anomaly, he had dared to wonder and to question and to dream, and his reward is a jolt back into the confines of his ordinary identity.

I have to this point identified Autonomy and Anomaly as the essentials of full human being, and while I have proposed one simple but highly effective method of activating these virtues, namely, the abolition of timepieces from our daily routines, my illustrations have in the main shown how our thoughts and behaviors — inculcated as they are — make Autonomy and Anomaly very difficult indeed. In fact, these virtues may seem to you virtually impossible to achieve. Let me now tell you how to achieve the impossible. We are doing it here at Watt Industries, and as I shall explain, even those who are not working in our ideal circumstances, indeed, anyone in any environment, can create new vitality and new success for themselves.

I have already said that when you join Watt Industries, you will have no job. Now I must clarify this remarkable statement, addressing my new workforce directly. You must think of your employment here as a journey from place to place within the world of diverse occupations. You will begin the journey at whatever available place which you are initially qualified to occupy, perhaps, let us say, as a scrivener. You will be trained by an experienced scrivener, and then spend an unspecified quantity of days becoming adept at the activities for maintaining this place. When you become capable enough to train another scrivener, that you shall do, and then you shall leave for another place, having prepared yours for a new occupant. Your next place will be of a quite different sort, perhaps as an assembler on the factory line. Once again, you will be trained by the man who has preceded you to this place, and you must train your replacement before you are permitted to depart.

Few men realize that training one's replacement is a practice essential to the effective functioning of any business enterprise, even one smaller and less variegated than Watt Industries. For only by instructing another successfully can one demonstrate complete mastery of any skill or subject, and thus qualify oneself to move on to fresh challenges and rewards. As Joseph Joubert so wisely said, "To teach is to learn twice."

Reading these words, many of you are moved to put down this book. You are clinging fiercely to the idea of yourself as "irreplaceable". You are thinking, "I have an obligation to myself to hold onto my duties and my place. Once I have attained a position of some expertise and authority, I would do all I can to keep it. Preparing the way for a replacement is either an admission of failure, or plain foolishness." You are not alone in these thoughts. They are held by the public at large, which remains almost entirely unhappy even as all of its members cling to their "places". You must see these resistant thoughts of yours for what they are, severe limitations upon any chance for the great achievement which I will describe to you as we continue. That great achievement is possible for anyone who joins our company, indeed, for anyone who can practice each day the principles I am describing in these pages.

For those of you who join Watt Industries, the variety of places that you will occupy here over the years is immense. You will, for instance, spend some time as a forester cutting the lumber with which our buildings and furniture are constructed, and as a miner excavating the minerals that are forged into the tools and machines that bear the Watt stamp. You will, in effect, become a roving citizen in the great chain of events that defines the life of our common enterprise.

In this way, you will move regularly from the *known* into the *unknown*, armed with the knowledge gained from your former place as you enter the new. You will develop habits of intellectual and behavioral flexibility, as well as a broad view of the range of activities that coincide in the large universe that our business embraces. Your mind will burst from the confines of its small room into a brightly lit expanse. And most importantly, you will be led to discover the principle that materializes from the conjunction of Autonomy and Anomaly: *INSPIRATION.*

You must acknowledge, as I continue, that the world is an assemblage of connections. No one and no thing exists in a state of sheer independence. The chair you are sitting on originated from a mighty oak which, once a seedling, required the sun and rain and fertile soil for its growth. It has grown from an Inspiration of productive and benevolent elements, from wind and water to industrial manpower and architectural intelligence. And just as this chair is a product of such Inspirations, so is any *new idea*. What is a new idea, after all, than the Inspiration of experiences and information in an original way? I shall illustrate this proposition with a story: One day some forty years ago, one of the pulp boilers from our paper production plant came to me in a profoundly excited state. He had previously worked as a chemist in one of our laboratories, and as a scrivener in our law office. In the laboratory, he had become particularly interested in the properties of salts formed from sulfuric acid; and in the law office, he had become particularly annoyed at the coarseness of the paper upon which he was expected to exact clean copies. On this day, he shared with me what was then the wisp of an idea, that a certain kind of sulfuric acid salt — called a sulfate — would remove impurities from the wood pulp remarkably well, and improve the purity of our paper and the clarity of our documents. As is my consistent practice, I encouraged him to pursue this idea, and the result is the smooth page you are reading at this moment.[†]

[†] EDITOR'S NOTE: *The page that you are reading at this very moment in the 1990s is even finer than Clement Watt might have imagined because of the further improvement of this very same sulfate process.*

This man arrived at a moment of profound Inspiration, thus: by clearing his mind of the ordinary
thoughts that close up our lives; by virtue of the
extra-ordinary atmosphere of employment here at
Watt Industries; and as a consequence of roving
the processes and activities of production, much as
a world traveller explores the terrain that forms our
continents. As you might imagine, my fellow in-
dustrialists thought then and think now that this
policy signals some mental disease on my part.
"Watt must be crazy," they say. "He takes a perfectly good, well-behaved scrivener, forces him to
teach the job to somebody else, and moves him
around to do a little bit of this and a little bit of
that. Such a worker surely would either quit in
exasperation, or, as with this upstart, try to take
over the company operations." Let me answer
their objection, which is the thoroughly predictable product of thoroughly predictable minds, by
pointing out two facts: first, no one has ever
elected to leave Watt Industries. Knowing that
they will enjoy both variety and opportunity, all

capable people who enter this family, stay. Second, when I require each worker to train his replacement, I am in effect seeing to it that each of them trains as *my* replacement. In other words, I am seeing to it that everyone eventually knows the scope of my operation so thoroughly that he is able to contemplate executive decisions. If thus training my own replacements is crazy, then so be it. However, it is perfectly true that a workforce of broadly-informed, broadly-experienced individuals makes for greater progress and productivity than a workforce of insulated dullards.

Let me not convey the mistaken impression here that the broad experience and training which encourages Inspiration leads inevitably to some practical invention and career success, as in the case I have described. Rather, Inspiration brings about a state of being that is infinitely more beneficial than any material product: It is *UNDERSTANDING*. And this, finally, is what I am offering to you as you join us: the fulfillment of your heart's true desire, to Understand your place in this universe. To see yourself not as a lowly creature stuck in the mud of common thoughts and behaviors, of bewilderment and fear, but as a dynamic particle of energy and intelligence aglow with the knowledge of your connectedness to all things, and confident in the limitlessness of your existence. Some day, your new selfhood may result in the acquisition of monetary wealth, as it has for me. You will come to know, however, that the real wealth lies within, in your very capacity, as Mr Walt Whitman has said, to "add, fuse, complete, extend — and celebrate the immortal and the good."

I MUST REVIEW and advance my remarks to this point, with the realization that not all the readers of this document are workers at Watt Industries, and further, to correct the impression that the achievement of Understanding is only possible for those who work under the conditions I have created. First, to review: *In order to leave the common herd, one must enact the principles of Autonomy and Anomaly, which practiced regularly create an atmosphere of Inspiration, the product of which is Understanding.*

Two maxims guarantee success in this regard: 1) Do not merely "kill" time, *animate* it. 2) Train your replacement, in the process of moving from "job" to "job" in the broad world of experience. I have attended to ways in which anyone might activate the first maxim. It is the second, and greater of the two, whose implementation must be clarified. Consider three persons who do not have the benefit of working at Watt Industries: 1) A sales clerk in a small gift shop. 2) A housewife, in fact, the very housewife whose troubles we have been following. 3) A fourteen year old schoolboy, very like the one we have come to know.

The sales clerk does not, of course, work under the injunction to train his replacement. Were he asked to do so, he would presume that his dismissal was imminent. Yet even in the realization that his job is secure, he is filled with dull anxiety. To him I say this: Regardless of what your employer requires of you, *prepare mentally* to train your replacement. As you proceed through your workday, rehearse in your mind the very words you would speak to another if he were standing by your side, eager to learn. Even in the most simple and apparently most obvious of activities, for instance, as you turn the key in the lock of your establishment upon entering in the morning, say to yourself, as if addressing another:

You must grasp the key firmly, and press it gently but decisively into the latch. You will feel it settle into its place. If not, a bit of wiggling should do the trick, thus. Then turn one-quarter revolution to the right, until you hear a solid click. The door is now unlocked, but to remove the key you must return it to its initial position. Place it securely in your vest pocket before turning the knob and entering, lest you absentmindedly leave it on a counter inside for anyone to pick up.

By rehearsing such activities as you perform them, you will *keep yourself in the present moment*, instead of mentally hurtling ahead past what you are doing, oblivious to the experience. You will see and feel your every action with renewed intensity, and begin watching with interest those tasks that had seemed to be empty routines. You will realize the beautiful complexity of even the smallest movement. You will appreciate your mastery at every instant. After some little while, you will find yourself able to rehearse your own sales process to yourself even as you are performing it, mentally stating your every action and explaining to yourself your every utterance while you are convincing a customer of the beauty and value of a pewter candy dish.

As amazing and complex as such a marvelous achievement seems, it will eventually take place, if you persist as if your replacement were at your side. Inevitably, you will begin to notice facets of your occupation that others do not. And just as inevitably, you will begin to *innovate*. Seeing your occupation with new eyes, you will notice details that heretofore went unknown, Inspiration that fills the day, details that none of your colleagues or customers or employers, with their ordinary powers of observation, could ever see. With new understanding and clarity about the actions you had been performing routinely, you will exhibit the renewed vitality and intellectual facility of one who has achieved Autonomy. Though the others will notice some striking improvement in your carriage, they will not detect your secret. Rather, they will regard you as an Anomaly, an exuberant master of his tasks. And you can be sure that, when the opportunity for greater responsibility and rewards presents itself, you will be a candidate. However, even if a career promotion does not eventuate, you will still be traveling apart from and above the others, a man who, in the act of "training his replacement", has opened his own eyes and found new happiness.

What of our young lady? Were she instructed to train her replacement, she would suppose no less than her husband had taken another wife! Her I also bid to behave through each of every day's tasks as if a domestic novice were by her side, whom she must expertly instruct. If she does so, even the mundane *act* of peeling a potato is transformed into an *art*. With this designation, I am aware of the present day tendency to use the word "art" to refer to any number of trivial deeds. I do not mean to do so here. For any one who fully attends to the present moment in the course of any act, whether it is the mellifluous piping of a flute, the steady and patient molding of the sculptor's clay, the counting out of shining coins at the teller's window, the gentle placement of a tulip bulb into the earth, or the preparation of food for our human sustenance, gives to that act the qualities of art, namely, concentration and beauty. As our young lady instructs her invisible replacement, she necessarily applies greater concentration to her work, and develops a new and immediate sense of beauty and intricacy even to the fastening of a button to a shirt. As with our store clerk, this young lady will be led by and by to the innovation of her duties. Then her friends will begin to wonder why our young lady seems to have more spring in her step. Further, they will wonder why she need not spend all day on domestic tasks, but finds time to venture out to the park and the library. It is because the by-products of her new vitality are efficiency and its consort, freedom. To the ordinary mind, training one's replacement may seem a burden, and training one's imaginary replacement may seem an insanity, but the truth is that this exercise will set you free from the thoughts and attitudes that have been ruling your every moment, and free you for the pursuit of new and different opportunities. Practiced consistently, this simple exercise offers you, in effect, a new life!

Our young scholar may take advantage of a uniquely practical opportunity for the actual training of his "replacement". It should be evident that every schoolroom is filled with students who would benefit from some improvement on the training that passes for education in the hands of their teachers. There are some classroom teachers who are positively inspired and electrifying as educators, true enough, but the common run is common indeed, and will never raise students above a common level of understanding. In the face of this mediocrity, if our young scholar were to become a *mentor* to another in his class, reviewing with that fortunate friend each day's lessons in such a way that would both clarify them and invest them with exhilarating relevance, then both would benefit mightily. The mentor would find himself newly alert to his books and his teacher, for they would provide the basic content for the additional instruction he would provide.

In addition, he would find himself gratified to discover an outlet for his imagination. Instead of being rapped on the knuckles for imagining his geometry lesson intruding into a lecture on history and geography, he would be encouraged to use that same imagination to present dull subjects in more interesting and unusual ways to his "replacement". He could illustrate, for instance, that a trade route running along the "hypotenuse" of a geographical area may be the shortest distance between two points. The "replacement" might then inquire whether this is always true. Taking the question as an opportunity to demonstrate deeper thought and further mastery of the subject, our mentor might then think to point out that geometry and geography do not always cooperate: a short distance may be full of impassable terrain, making it a bad line to travel in the world of practical affairs. Training another, as this illustration suggests, must entail spontaneous questions that challenge one's knowledge and imagination.

Every question posed to any teacher is an opportunity for that teacher to develop greater clarity and to grow intellectually in the act of explanation. However, every question is also a somewhat fearsome occasion, because it may pull the teacher *into the unknown*, into mental territory that he has not deliberately prepared to address. This is why most teachers do not welcome, indeed often forbid, questions from their students. This is also why our young mentor must encourage his "trainee" to pose all manner of questions, because our young mentor must learn to respond to the unknown thoughtfully and fearlessly. This is an equally crucial matter for our store clerk and our young lady. However, since each of them is educating an imaginary replacement, each must both create and respond to the questions such a replacement might conceivably ask. Thus, as the young lady folds a shirt, she must not only explain the process to her internal auditor, she must also give good reasons for her every move. As she says, "first fold the right sleeve diagonally across the back," our young lady must hear a voice ask "Why," and to this voice she must reply.

BY WAY OF SUMMARY, let me say that training one's replacement, both actual and imaginary, must include occasions for addressing the unknown. To assure that such occasions arise in imaginary situations, one must add to each and every directive the word "because", which obligates the addition of a good reason. There will come times, more than any of us realize before we experience them, when we can give no good reason for an action. Our young lady may find, for instance, that she cannot explain why she folds a sleeve as she does, except to note that her mother did it this way, and her mother's mother as well. To appeal to tradition thus as one's only rationale is to admit that one is behaving mechanically and thoughtlessly. Training one's replacement means not only describing the techniques that comprise one's occupation, but also making certain that no technique is merely arbitrary.

In the course of this advice, I have suggested

that those who follow it may enjoy a number of benefits. However, I must add that *performing this exercise with such benefits in view may only undermine them*. This must seem a great contradiction: I am saying that in order to achieve the goals of greater freedom and happiness and wealth *you must act without those goals in mind*. Contradictory as it may seem, this is an important requirement. Anyone in pursuit of a goal cannot possibly pay attention to the present moment. Further, anyone in pursuit of a particular goal may miss the appearance of an alternate, and perhaps greater, opportunity.

I will illustrate with a final story about a young student who decided that he wanted to become a messenger boy for the local newspaper. Having read in one of my publications about the benefits of becoming a mentor to a fellow student, he set to tutoring a classmate in English composition, with the supposition that sharpening his skills with written and oral communication would place him in contention for the position he sought. One afternoon, the editor of *Harper's* magazine was touring the school, contemplating a piece on the modern state of education. As he passed our young mentor and his classmate, huddled in concentration in the school library, the editor stopped to overhear the mentor's excited whisperings, and read over his shoulder some of the sample paragraphs the boy had composed for instructional purposes. The editor realized quickly that this student already had the makings of an adept journalist, and called him aside. "What position do you aspire to?" asked the editor. "Messenger boy," said the student, with absolutely ridiculous certainty. "Is there no other occupation you might entertain?" asked the editor. "Of course not, sir," insisted our goal-obsessed fellow. With some effort, the editor convinced the young man to accept a part-time position as a junior copy editor, at a salary five times more generous than that of a messenger boy. And today, this former mentor is himself the senior editor of *Harper's*, and laughs nervously when reminded that had he continued

APPLY THE SECRET you have learned here in all your affairs. All who do cannot help but prosper. Teach this secret to your loved ones. From the executive suite to the assembly line, the kitchen to the classroom, everything will change for you. These few pages are the doorway to any success you seek.

Now you have in your hands the procedures that will assure you the fulfillment of your heart's desires.

— *Clement Watt,* 1919